THIS BOOK RECORDS THE FIRST YEARS OF

_____

◇ ◆ ◇

Baby
Record
Book

Illustrations by Lucy Su

❖ ❖ ❖

Text by Karen Farrington

BLITZ EDITIONS

CONTENTS

◇ ◇ ◇

FAMILY TREE

With every new addition comes a fresh branch on the family tree.
Record previous generations here, they will fascinate
your child in years to come.

Grandfather (maternal)   Grandfather (paternal)

_____   _____

Grandmother (maternal)   Grandmother (paternal)

Uncles and Aunts

_____   _____

_____   _____

Cousins

_____   _____

_____   _____

Mother

Father

Baby

Sisters

Brothers

First Hours

After months of waiting, baby has arrived. All the anticipation and anxiety
about your unborn baby vanish as you hold your little bundle close for the first
time. For parents there is soaring joy, excitement – and relief too!
Note down details of that unforgettable moment here.

Date and day of birth

Did baby cry?

Time

Baby's special features

Place

Baby's first clothes

Father's first thought

Due date

Delivered by

Mother's first thought

Weight

Other comments

Length

Head measurement

Birth registered (place and date)

Hair?

WELCOME
TO
OUR WORLD

✧ ✧ ✧

A new baby spreads happiness and hope among everyone. It's not only mum and dad who cherish the first hours and days of the new arrival. After the drama of the delivery is over, close family and friends are longing for their first glimpse of baby's bright eyes and tiny toes. With them comes a shower of good wishes and gifts, each rattle, matinee jacket and pair of bootees carefully chosen to say in a special way: 'We're pleased to meet you'. Mum often finds herself festooned with beautiful blooms and, who knows, maybe some champagne by way of congratulations. Amid all the excitement it is easy to forget who featured in those first few days. On the next page, write down your list of visitors and the names of those who sent gifts and flowers.

Visitors and presents

COMING HOME

Today is the start of your time together as a family.
Soon you will not recall what life was like
without having a baby to love.

Bonds which will last a lifetime are being forged in these initial weeks.
Ahead lies laughter, sharing, caring – and a few tears. Take each day and
night as it comes and enjoy this first adventure in the world together.

Date and time

Was baby awake or asleep?

Weather

Describe the nursery

How did you get home?

What was baby wearing?

Was anyone there to greet you both?

When did baby feed?

Photographs

Telling The World

◇ ◇ ◇

It's time to broadcast the good news.
Anyone who knows you have been
pregnant will be eager to hear the
details. Some people advertise in local
or national newspapers while others
send cards to distant relatives and far
flung friends. Just picture their faces
breaking into huge smiles after they pick
up the card from the doormat and read
all about baby. Don't forget to include
all of baby's vital statistics: full name,
weight and date and time of birth.
Attach your chosen card and published
newspaper advertisement on
the next page.

Arrival card
◇ ◆ ◇
Newspaper cutting

BABY FIRSTS

Every day brings a new discovery for infants. They grow ever
more aware of what is going on around them – and
strive to be a part of it.

Before them lies a huge array of 'firsts' to thrill them. And for parents
it is a magical time too. Babies are an endless fascination. Who would have
thought a baby sucking its thumb for the first time could be such a wonderful
sight? Yet your heart thuds with pride at every early achievement, equally
vital as those of later years. Record those moments here before
they are lost in the mists of time.

First smile

First finds hands

Who was it for?

First finds feet

First focuses on a moving object

Grips rattle or toy for the first time

First looks in a mirror

First reaches out for you

First recognises name

First moves to music

First tooth

First haircut

First party invitation

First time on the potty

First dry day

First dry night

LULLABY

A peacefully sleeping baby is a vision of loveliness, a little angel. Some babies may seem more wakeful than others but in time parents hit on a winning bedtime formula. Sometimes it is a favourite story or song; or you may have to kiss umpteen toys goodnight! Eventually even the most determined baby will succumb, lulled by the stroking hand or the soothing voice of a loved one.

How long did your baby sleep each day:

at 1 week? _____

at 2 weeks? _____

at 3 weeks? _____

at 4 weeks? _____

at 5 weeks? _____

at 6 weeks? _____

at 6 months? _____

at 12 months? _____

When did baby first sleep
through the night?

_____

When did daytime naps stop?

_____

First night in own room?

_____

Did baby have a comforter?

_____

Did baby have a favourite
bedtime routine?

_____

_____

Favourite lullaby?

_____

Describe baby's bedtime toys

_____

_____

RUB-A-DUB-DUB

There's much more to bathtime than simply washing. Ask any baby
about the happy, splashy time to be had in the tub. The simplest things can provide
endless fun – cups for pouring, bottles for squirting. As a special treat, add
a little bubble bath and let baby splash in the foam.

When did baby first enjoy a bath?

_____

Describe the first bath

_____

_____

When did baby first join you in the bath?

_____

Use a big bath alone?

_____

What were baby's favourite bath toys?

_____

_____

And best loved bath time song?

_____

Photographs

NAMING DAY

The gathering of family and friends at baby's
naming ceremony is a joyful tradition.

A christening evokes many joyous images. A baby in a flowing robe, ribbons on flowers, bows on gifts, church bells ringing out to welcome a newborn. Solemn vows are taken by parents and godparents, the people charged with helping to steer the child through life's passage. Family and friends love to gather for this spiritually significant occasion.

Some parents prefer a naming day, a less formal introduction to the world but equally heartfelt. For others, it's a party to honour the newcomer. Whichever you choose, it's a momentous day in a young life.

Baby's full name

_____

Meaning of names

_____

Date and place

_____

Your baby wore

_____

The celebration was held at

_____

How did your baby react?

_____

Guests

_____

_____

_____

Presents

_____

_____

_____

SPECIAL PEOPLE

◇ ◇ ◇

For baby, mum and dad are the centre of the world. The broadest grins and
most loving giggles are reserved for them. But others form an essential
circle of love, trust and friendship on which your baby will grow to depend.
There may be older brothers and sisters who will fascinate a young
baby with their antics. Also, there may be more siblings to come later.
Anyone your baby sees on a daily or weekly basis will soon forge a close
bond which will endure for the months and years ahead.
Remember those people your baby loved best here.

Brothers

Uncles

Neighbours

Sisters

Nanny or carer

Aunts

Other special friends

Photographs

PLAY TIME

◇ ◇ ◇

Children learn through play – and it's fun as well. In the early days mum and dad are the best gymnasium, providing support for shaky limbs. Soon household objects and toys will become a major source of interest, holding baby's rapt attention as balls roll, bricks stack, cupboards empty, water splashes. Then it's 'let's pretend', with baby suddenly a policeman or a ballerina, a doctor or nurse, a goody or baddy. It's hard to believe so much progress can be made in such a short time.

When did baby first play
peek-a-boo?

_____

First swipe at a hanging toy?

_____

First go after a rolling ball?

_____

First stack building bricks?

_____

First look at a book?

_____

First play a toy instrument?

_____

First play a pretend game?

_____

First use a swing?

_____

First ride a tricycle?

_____

FAVOURITE TOYS

◇ ◇ ◇

Who can tell which plaything will capture
the imagination of your child? A garish
purple dragon may seem the height of
hideousness to you when to your child it is
an object to be loved, petted and cuddled,
no matter how chewed and dog-eared it
becomes. It is not only fluffy animals that
children seize on as favourites. Toy cars,
wooden trains, rubber balls and even pint-
sized vacuum cleaners may all become top
of the popular toys, dragged up to bed and
snuggled up to. Each will be christened
and lavished with love.

Favourite fluffy toy

_____

Its name

_____

Favourite wheeled toy

_____

Favourite toy at 3 months/9 months

_____

Favourite toy at 18 months/2 years

_____

Bedtime companion

_____

Its name

_____

Where did it come from?

_____

Oddest 'toy'

_____

LET'S GO

◆ ◇ ◆

Stepping out of the door with baby for the first time is a proud moment –
even if it's taken hours to get ready. The simplest outing will provide
interest and stimulation for your baby, whether it is a walk in
the park, feeding the ducks or a trip to the local shop.
Record details of your first outing here.

Where did you go?

_____

How did baby travel?

_____

And what did your baby wear?

_____

Awake or asleep?

_____

First time in a buggy

_____

First time without a buggy

_____

First time on a bus

_____

First time on a train

_____

First time in the park

_____

First fed the ducks

_____

First visit to a playgroup

_____

First visit to a friend

_____

Other first outings/dates

_____   _____

_____   _____

_____   _____

_____   _____

_____   _____

_____   _____

First Foods

When milk alone is not enough to satisfy baby's hunger, it's time to start
on solid food — an exciting, if messy, time.

First solid food served

_____

What was it?

_____

Where did baby sit?

_____

What was the reaction?

_____

Final breast or bottle feed

_____

Favourite meal at six months

_____

First finger food held at

_____

Spoon first held at

_____

First drank from a covered beaker

_____

First drank from open cup

_____

First meal in a cafe or restaurant

_____

Favourite drink

_____

Favourite main meal

_____

Favourite fruit

_____

Most hated food

_____

Favourite treat

_____

HAPPY TALK

❖ ❖ ❖

As soon as your baby arrives you launch
into conversations but, of course, they are
all one way! It doesn't take long, however,
for your baby to discover the pleasures of
creating sounds and he or she will soon
want to chatter back, even if you cannot
understand all that is being said.
As a parent you will learn to recognise the
meaning of a full range of coos and grunts,
even if no one else can. It is a wonderful
moment when your baby begins to talk
into a play telephone, one of their first
departures into the land of make-believe.

When did baby first coo?

_____

When was the first repeated noise,
like ga-ga?

_____

When was the first laugh?

_____

And the first shout to attract
your attention?

_____

When did your baby start
using a play telephone?

_____

Record the date of the first word

_____

And the first animal noise (moo, woof)

_____

FIRST FRIENDS

✧ ✧ ✧

Playmates form an ever-increasing place of importance in your child's
world. With another young one, they will learn the value of sharing toys,
playing pretend and laughing too, at first alongside each other, then
together. But when you are young anyone or anything can become a firm
friend. A family cat or dog – or one that lives nearby – is often adored by
a baby. There may be a toy or doll with whom he or she regularly chats.
Some children even have an imaginary friend complete with name and
appetite... you may find your child asking for two biscuits, one for
himself and one for an invisible pal.

First boy friend

_____

First girl friend

_____

Best friend at 1 year

_____

Best friend at 2 years

_____

Cat

_____

Dog

_____

Other pets

_____

_____

_____

_____

Invisible friend

_____

Photographs

Favourite Things

❖ ❖ ❖

It won't be long before your baby gives a
clear indication of just what he or she
likes – and loathes. Giving your baby the
power of choice helps them to assert their
budding characters. Attachments form
quickly between a baby and toy, T-shirt,
dinner dish or even a television programme.
As for dislikes, they can range from food to
hairwashing, teeth cleaning and even
colours. Giving your child what he or she
likes doesn't mean spoiling them. Children
have preferences just as we do, and it is
only natural to consider their views.

Favourite rough and tumble games

_____

Favourite soothing habit
eg thumb sucking

_____

Favourite fun activity, eg
swimming or gym

_____

Favourite book at 18 months

_____

Top television programme at 2

_____

Favourite video at 2

_____

Favourite colour

_____

Preferred clothes

_____

Most disliked clothes

_____

Most loathed activity

_____

Others

_____

SUMMER FUN

Sea, frothy surf, soft sand and shells— the beach is a glorious adventure
playground for your baby. Remember those first golden moments
at the seaside here.

Date of first beach visit

First paddle

_____

Where was it?

First sandcastle

_____

Who came too?

First swim in the sea

_____

Did baby like the water?

First collected shells

_____

Did baby like the sand?

First donkey ride

_____

SETTING OFF

◇ ◇ ◇

It's not much fun looking at the world from lying flat on your back. So it's not surprising that babies start a crusade to get on the move from when they are just a few weeks old. First step towards getting up and away happens at around two months, when they hold their heads up unsupported. From there it is on to rolling, sitting, crawling and then walking, which gives them a much-valued independence.

First holds head up

_____

First roll

_____

First press-up to tummy

_____

Sits unsupported

_____

Crawls

_____

Stands holding onto something

_____

Cruises around the furniture

_____

Climbs the stairs

_____

Walks unaided

_____

ART WORK

From the moment babies grasp a crayon they are keen to make
their mark. Paste your baby's first drawing on the
next page. Don't forget to date it!

When did your baby first hold a crayon?

_____

Make a scribble?

_____

Use finger paints?

_____

Use play dough?

_____

Use a paint brush?

_____

Hold a pencil 'properly'?

_____

Do a recognisable drawing?

_____

Draw a face?

_____

Draw a body?

_____

Sign his own drawing?

_____

First work of art

PARTY PIECES

All the world's a stage to a growing baby, who will thrive on showing off
the latest tricks to an appreciative audience.

First waves bye-bye

_____

First claps hands

_____

First jumps

_____

Recites first nursery rhyme

_____

Sings first song

_____

Removes bits of clothing, eg socks

_____

Puts on clothing unaided

_____

Dresses up

_____

First dances

Others

First practical joke

First pretends

· Photographs ·

CELEBRATIONS

Introducing your baby to the traditions you love is a vital ritual and one
you will enjoy. Suddenly, you see age-old celebrations through new eyes, as
your baby does. Babies bring a delightful extra dimension to a festivity
that everyone can share. Monitor their every response, from the elation of
tasting a first chocolate Easter egg to the wonder of gazing through a
window as fireworks burst in the sky above. For them it is only the
beginning of a childhood in which they will look forward to every year's
special dates with relish.

What happened on Mothers Day?

What happened on Father's Day?

_____

And Mother's birthday?

And Father's birthday?

_____

How did you celebrate baby's
first Easter?

_____

Where, and who was there?

_____

How did you mark Firework night?

_____

Other important festivals during
baby's first year

_____

Photographs

THE FIRST NOEL

Christmas is for children and even the smallest baby will make the festive celebrations complete. The enchantment on their faces when they see a Christmas tree for the first time spangled with twinkling lights, glittering tinsel and shiny baubles is enough to make any heart lurch.

Where did you spend baby's first
Christmas Day?

_____

Who with?

_____

What gift did you give your baby?

_____

Did baby have a special
Christmas dinner?

_____

What other presents did baby get?

_____

What did baby enjoy best?

_____

Photographs

HAPPY BIRTHDAY TO YOU

◇ ◇

It's astonishing how soon this special day arrives. For most mums, it seems like only weeks ago that the newborn was lying tiny and helpless in a cot. Twelve months on and they are robust, rampaging tots with plenty of skills already mastered, just waiting for the next challenge. They may not know what all the fuss is about but their little eyes will still shine at the sight of a cake, a candle and a chorus of 'Happy Birthday'. Spend a few quiet moments alone as well, to reflect on the first year of your baby's life.

How did you celebrate?

_____

Where?

_____

Who was there?

_____

_____

_____

What did you buy baby?

_____

What other gifts arrived?

_____

What was your baby's reaction?

_____

Describe the cake

_____

How did you feel?

_____

Photographs

PREDICTIONS

From the moment you become pregnant, you are full of hopes and dreams for your baby. If your pregnant bump was a lively little mover you will probably already have picked a future for it on the football field or disco dancing floor. In the early days it is a parent's prerogative to toy with careers and vocations for the newborn. There may even be family traditions which you hope they will follow. Write down what you want for them and why and capture those dreams forever. Then when your child makes its own way in the world you can compare your first thoughts with what has actually happened. In a few years ask your child what he or she imagines the future holds. The thoughts of a child, often quaint and curious, will make emotive reading, especially when they have children of their own.

Your Predictions

_____   _____

_____   _____

_____   _____

_____   _____

_____   _____

_____   _____

_____   _____

Your Child's Predictions

_____   _____

_____   _____

_____   _____

_____   _____

_____   _____

_____   _____

MEDICAL
RECORDS

◆ ◆ ◆

For the health and well-being of
your baby, keep a note of the illnesses
contracted and the immunisations
received. Remember, immunisation
timetables may vary around the country.

◆ VACCINATIONS ◆

Triple vaccine (diphtheria,
tetanus and whooping cough)

First injection _____

Second injection _____

Third injection _____

Measles, mumps and rubella

_____

Polio

_____

Hib

_____

BCG

_____

Booster for diphtheria, tetanus,
whooping cough and polio (pre-school)

_____

⬦ ILLNESSES ⬦

Chicken pox

_____

Measles or mumps

_____

Allergies (and reactions)

_____

_____

_____

NHS number

_____

Other notes

_____

_____

GROWING UP

Record your baby's height and weight with two different coloured lines
on the chart opposite. Sometimes your baby will shoot up from one month
to the next – at other times you will worry that there is no progress!
But by the end of the first year you will be astonished by the
progress of your infant.